Rocky Bear Meets Jesus

Rocky Bear Meets Jesus

52 Stories that Teach Christian Living

Robert H. Ramey, Jr.

Ramey Publishing Company
Pinehurst, NC

Rocky Bear Meets Jesus
52 Stories that Teach Christian Living
by Robert H. Ramey, Jr.

Published by:
Ramey Publishing Company
Pinehurst, NC

Orders: rhramey@mindspring.com

ISBN 0-9772941-3-7 (13 digit: 978-0-9772941-3-8)
Printed in the United States of America

Library of Congress Control Number: 2005909475

Book Design: Bookcovers.com

To my nine grandchildren:

Georgia Parris
Tesh Parris
Jane Robbins Mize
Ramey Mize
Garrison Ramey
Mitchell Ramey
Claire Dorrier
Reese Dorrier
and
Jay Dorrier

. . .

who are a delight!

Contents

Part Three: Mother's Day through Summer

Acknowledgments

My list of acknowledgments, though short, is heartfelt. My journey around the Sandhills of North Carolina has embraced a number of interim and temporary supply relationships at various churches. They include both the Vass and Cypress Presbyterian Churches in Vass, Bethesda Presbyterian Church in Aberdeen, Marks Creek Presbyterian Church in Hamlet, First Presbyterian Church in Carthage, Jackson Springs Presbyterian Church in Jackson Springs, Brownson Memorial Presbyterian Church in Southern Pines, Community Presbyterian Church in Pinehurst, Eureka Presbyterian Church in Whispering Pines, and The Congregational Church of Pinehurst.

For a long time members of these churches have encouraged me to put Rocky's adventures in book form. Their encouragement has finally come to fruition, and I want to thank them. I mention one young church member in particular, Kevin Dann, of the Jackson Springs Presbyterian Church. Kevin gave Rocky a box of Blueberry Morning cereal for Christmas, with this note:

"Dear Rocky Bear: I always knew you liked blueberries. That's why I'm giving you some Blueberry Morning. It's really good. I guess I have a bear appetite. Hope you like it. Have a good, hibernating Christmas and a great happy New Year. Sincerely, Kevin."

I am grateful to friends Jean Snively and Locke Bowman and also to my daughter Andrea Parris for proofreading my manuscript. Their work was indeed a labor of love.

And here is my most important acknowledgment: My wife, Gail, takes even more delight in Rocky than I do. She constantly searches for new "Rocky" material and supports me every step of the way. I mention Gail specifically because without her wonderful insight, humor, encouragement, and help I would never have finished this project.

Pinehurst, NC, 2005

Introduction

Years ago my wife, Gail, bought a teddy bear for one of my grandchildren. She also decided to buy another bear so that the grandchildren would have one to play with when they came to visit us. But what to name him?

At that time a man named Rocky came to work on our heating system. Crazily perhaps, we decided to name our new stuffed friend Rocky, too! Since then Rocky has steadily grown in importance in the life of our family. Only now he has extended his influence beyond our home. Shortly after we moved from Atlanta to the Sandhills of North Carolina, I started doing supply preaching at the Vass Presbyterian Church. I always included a sermon for the children in the service, a custom I began almost as soon as I started my ministry fifty years ago.

One day Gail said to me, "Why don't you take Rocky to Vass and make him the focal point of your talk with the children?" And so I did. The three children who came forward that day for my talk seemed to like Rocky. From then until now Rocky has been my constant companion wherever I have gone to conduct Sunday services.

People seem to have a special place in their hearts for teddy bears. When I visit nursing homes now, I notice that many residents have teddy bears in their rooms. Maybe they had those bears when they were growing up or they received them as recent gifts. Teddy bears seem to be everywhere.

When my own three children were growing up, they had Big Ted, a bear who was at the heart of my playtime with them. There in my own home I discovered the sheer delight children take in stuffed animals, especially teddy bears. And old shopworn Big Ted is still with our family!

And yet, adults like teddy bears equally well. On my travels around the Sandhills, people stop and ask me how Rocky is doing. My wife jokes that Rocky is much better known around here than she is!

Recently I was visiting St. Andrews-Covenant Presbyterian Church in Wilmington, about 150 miles from Southern Pines where I once served as a parish associate at Brownson Memorial Presbyterian Church. A couple from Brownson had just moved to Wilmington and were received into membership the day I visited the church. As they walked out, the man saw me sitting in an aisle seat, touched me on the arm, and said, "Did you bring your bear with you?"

Rocky gets Christmas and birthday cards at our address, even presents. Children sometimes draw his picture during a church service. They love to hold him until the end of the service and then return him to us. When friends send us any kind of card, they invariably pick out one with a bear on it. A 96-year-old member at Jackson Springs sent us holiday greetings one year on a beautiful Christmas card with a bear on the front.

I hope these stories will help introduce your children to the Christian faith in a simple, humorous way. They deal with everyday life situations we all face. Often we fumble our way through them just as Rocky does.

Parents can use the book as bedtime stories. Pastors may choose to adapt them as children's sermons, beginning with the first section and moving through the next summer. Older children, of course, may choose to read the stories at their leisure.

I have suggested relevant Scripture verses at the end of each story. Most of the verses are taken from the New Revised Standard Version except in a few cases where I quoted from The Message:The Bible in Contemporary Language by Eugene H. Peterson.

Rather than target the stories specifically for a five- or six-year-old age group, I tried to make them general enough to interest older children as well. Younger children, many of whom have stuffed friends of their own, can relate at some level to the stories because they like animals. However, older children will naturally better understand some of the story themes.

The setting for the stories is a vacant lot next to our home in Pinehurst. Rocky came from the mountains of North Carolina to live on that lot six years ago. Much of the time he sits by the lake snoozing and eating my blueberries. I usually visit Rocky on Saturdays, and he never fails to make the day interesting for me. I hope you find his adventures as interesting as I did. But more importantly, may you and your children receive help in living the Christian life as you identify with Rocky's struggles as a young bear.

Rocky Bear Meets Jesus

Rocky Leaves Home

Yesterday was a beautiful Saturday in Pinehurst. I was visiting my new friend Rocky Bear, who had just moved next door to my wife Gail and me.

"Tell me, Rocky," I began, "how you came to live on this vacant lot next to us."

"Well, Dr. Bob," Rocky replied, "I was living with my parents up in the North Carolina mountains. My sisters and brothers had already left home. I, too, felt a tug to move on. So I told my parents that it was great in the mountains, but I wanted to feel the sand beneath my paws!

"Papa Bear said, 'Okay, Rocky, we'll be sad to see you go. But we always knew you would leave someday. We hope you'll remember two things as you leave. First, please stay in touch with us. Also, remember to trust and obey God in everything.' Then Papa Bear and Mama Bear gave me a bear hug and waved goodbye. Soon I set out for the Sandhills of North Carolina."

"Did you have any interesting adventures along the way?" I asked.

"You bet I did!" Rocky said. "One day I saw a herd of deer eating berries on a hillside. Since I'm pretty big,

I knew I could growl at them and scare them away. Then I could eat all of their berries."

"So what happened?" I asked, as Rocky became more and more interesting.

"Well," Rocky said, "my parents taught me not to be mean to smaller animals, so I left them alone."

"That was kind of you, Rocky, not to pick on the deer," I said.

"Thank you," Rocky replied, "but I was still hungry. After traveling for many miles, I came to Jackson Springs. In a trash can I finally found some food I could eat. Then I kept walking and soon came to this vacant lot next to you. It was a tough trip, but I made it by trusting and obeying God."

"Good for you!" I told Rocky.

"It's great to be here," Rocky said. "Later I heard on the animal channel that those deer ate too many berries and got sick. I'm glad I was kind to them and obeyed God. Now I can enjoy eating *your* blueberries!"

"Yes," I said, "I just hope all of us can learn to trust and obey God, too. By the way, Rocky, please save a few of my blueberries for me!"

Scripture verse: "By an act of faith, Abraham said yes to God's call to travel to an unknown place that would become his home" (Heb. 11:8, Msg.).

Rocky Makes Some New Friends

When I visited Rocky yesterday, he told me he needed to make some new friends. I told him I would help him meet some of my other friends.

Daniel Duck was swimming by. I had seen him swimming in the lake for years. "Daniel," I said, "we have a new animal on the lot that I want you to meet . . . Rocky Bear!"

But Daniel was thinking to himself, "How can I ever play with this *big* bear?"

Rocky was thinking to himself, "How can I ever play with this *little* duck?" But soon they found that both of them liked to swim a lot. They knew they would be good swimming buddies!

In a few minutes Robert Rabbit came hopping by. "Robert," I said, "I want you to meet Rocky Bear, our new friend from the mountains."

Robert whispered something in Rocky's ear that I couldn't hear. He said, "Rocky, if you ever want any blueberries, go to Dr. Bob's yard. He has the best blueberries around here!"

"I already know that!" Rocky laughed.

Rocky was beginning to feel more at home since he had met two new animal friends. "Thanks for helping me meet Daniel and Robert," he said. "I hope you will be my friend, too, Dr. Bob."

"Sure, Rocky," I said. "Every Saturday I'll come over to visit you and see how you're getting along. Then on Sunday Gail and I would like to have you go to church with us. I know the boys and girls at church would love to meet you, too. I always tell them a story about something that has happened to me during the past week. Maybe I can tell them what we have been doing."

"I'll try it," Rocky said. So the next day Rocky went to Vass Church with us. The boys and girls loved Rocky and invited me to bring him back every Sunday.

On the way home from church I said, "Rocky, how did it go today?"

"At first," Rocky replied, "I didn't want to go. But everyone was so nice to me that soon I felt right at home."

"That's the way it is with church," I said. "We soon make many friends and feel right at home. And we meet God, too."

Scripture verse: "Become friends with God; he's already a friend with you" (2 Cor. 5:20, Msg.).

Rocky Meets Ramola Bear

Yesterday Rocky was so excited he was jumping up and down on his hind paws. "My, you are excited today, Rocky," I said.

"Yes, yes!" Rocky said. "I got up from my nap and rubbed my eyes. I couldn't believe what I was seeing down by the lake."

"What was it, Rocky?" I asked. "Tell me, my man."

"It was like a wonderful present," Rocky answered. "Down by the lake was a cute little girl bear. I really wanted to meet another bear around here. I had already met Daniel Duck and Robert Rabbit, so it was great to see her."

"And what's her name?" I asked.

"Ramola Bear," Rocky replied. "She was fishing when I first saw her. She taught me how to fish. With her paw she would reach down and scoop a fish right out of the water."

"So that's why you've been doing so much fishing lately," I laughed. "Maybe you won't be eating all of my blueberries now!"

"It's wonderful to have a new friend," Rocky said.

"Let me tell you a little story, Rocky," I said. "One day some of Jesus' disciples—Peter and Andrew and James and John—met him by a lake just as you met Ramola by a lake. They were happy to meet their new friend. He helped them catch a lot of fish. In fact, they caught so many fish that their nets began to break."

"Wow!" said Rocky. "That's more fish than Ramola and I caught!"

"I'm sure it is, Rocky," I answered. "Then Jesus told them that from now on he would help them 'catch' people and tell them about God."

"Did they decide to follow him?" Rocky asked.

"Yes," I replied. "An amazing thing happened. They left their boats, their homes—everything—and decided to follow Jesus. He was their friend for the rest of their lives. And he wants us to follow him, too, and to be his friend."

"That's a good story," Rocky said. "And I'm glad to have Ramola as my friend, too!"

Scripture verse: "And he got up, left everything, and followed him" (Luke 5:28).

Rocky Meets Another Newcomer

Yesterday I heard a lot of noise coming from next door. The animals were picking on Amy Aardvark, a newcomer. Amy had just escaped from the Asheboro Zoo by using her long, sharp claws to dig under a fence.

"You're the funniest looking animal I ever saw," Robert Rabbit said when he met Amy. "I can't tell whether you are a baby elephant or an anteater!"

"Nor can I," Rocky added. "That long snout of yours must get in the way."

Ramola Bear, Rocky's special friend, said, "We certainly don't need a floppy-eared female around here. Besides, this is *our* home."

Amy hung her head as tears trickled down her long face. I knew the animals sometimes said unkind things, but I had never heard anything like this. Looking right at Rocky, Robert, and Ramola, I said, "*All* of you are newcomers to this lot. When you moved here, we welcomed you and treated you with kindness. So how could you be so mean to Amy?"

"Oh," Rocky answered quickly, "it doesn't bother her to hear all this stuff."

"I'm sure it does," I shot back. "I don't think you

would like it either." Upset, I left and went home. I was sure Amy would be heading back to the Asheboro Zoo as fast as she could go. I hadn't been home five minutes when I heard a yelp that scared me out of my wits. Rocky was screaming at the top of his bear lungs.

"Rocky, Rocky," I called, running back to the lot, "what's wrong?"

"Dr. Bob, you won't believe this," Rocky said, "but I just sat down on a hill of *fire ants*. My bottom has been stung a million times or more!"

"Not to worry, Rocky," Amy said, "those ants are no problem." Quickly she started burrowing her long nose into the ground and eating the ants. In a few minutes she had cleaned them out.

"Amazing!" said Rocky. "I can't thank you enough."

"It was nothing," Amy replied. "Say, Dr. Bob, if your neighbors have trouble with termites, tell 'em to call me. I like termites as much as ants!"

"Hooray for Amy," the animals shouted. "Can you stay with us?"

So that's how Amy Aardvark came to live next door. Ramola Bear is getting a little jealous of all the interest Rocky is taking in Amy. After all, Amy is an anteater, a *cousin* to the bear family!

Scripture verse: "Welcome one another, therefore, just as Christ has welcomed you, for the glory of God" (Rom. 15:7).

Rocky and Duke

Yesterday I saw Duke wandering around the vacant lot next door. It was only a few weeks ago that Duke, a pitiful stray dog, had appeared. Covered with fleas, he had dozens of sticky burrs caught in his fur. He also had sore places on his back where his fur had come off from briars and thistles. Would the animals be better to him than they were to Amy Aardvark? Had they learned anything?

Yes! Daniel Duck brought a special weed from the lake and put it on Duke's sores. The weed quickly made Duke's sores feel so much better.

Then Amy Aardvark herself sucked up all of Duke's fleas in her long snout. She liked fleas almost as much as fire ants and termites!

But Duke was hungry, too. He hadn't had a good meal in weeks. Rocky took him in and gave him some bread covered with the best honey Duke had ever tasted. Duke got better every day.

One day Duke and I were talking with Rocky. Duke thanked Rocky for helping him, saying, "If it weren't for you, Rocky, I would never have made it."

To Duke's surprise, and mine as well, Rocky said, "Oh, well, that was then, but this is now."

"What do you mean, Rocky?" I asked. "I don't understand."

"Well," Rocky replied."I think I'll just quit trying to help others. Sometimes I try so hard to help them that others make fun of me. It takes a lot of my time when I could be fishing and looking for honey . . ."

"And eating my blueberries!" I added."Rocky, I suppose all of us feel like quitting sometimes. We wonder whether we ought to keep on doing good things for others. But God wants us to keep on doing the right thing. A man in the Bible named Paul said for us not to grow tired of being good and kind. Where would Duke be now if you and Amy and Daniel had not been kind to him?"

"I guess that's true," Rocky said.

"It's always right to do what God wants us to do," I said."I hope we'll never quit caring about others."

"But there is something I wish Duke would do," Rocky said."I wish he would change his name to *Carolina*!"

Scripture verse:"So let us not grow weary in doing what is right . . ." (Gal. 6:9a).

Note: The author confesses to being a sports fan of the University of North Carolina!

Rocky and Labor Day

Yesterday I found Rocky sleeping peacefully under a pine tree. However, my footsteps woke him up. "Happy Labor Day, Rocky!" I said.

"What's Labor Day, Dr. Bob?" Rocky asked.

"Well," I replied, "we thank God for our jobs and the chance to work and to serve others."

"But I don't like to work!" Rocky said.

"I've noticed that," I replied, laughing heartily. "You always come and eat *my* blueberries instead of hunting for berries in the woods. You don't seem to want to do anything you don't have to do."

"You've got that right, Dr. Bob," Rocky said. "But I have to take a lot of naps. I'm a growing bear. And I have to get ready for a long winter. But maybe I can do better. What can I do to improve?"

"Rocky," I replied, "I saw on TV that bears like to eat insects, berries, nuts, and grasses."

"Wait just a minute, Dr. Bob!" Rocky said, "I never could get too worked up about eating bugs. But I do like berries, nuts, and grasses."

"All right, then," I said, "I want you to come over and eat that grass that is growing under our shrubs. That would help us a great deal."

"Okay," Rocky answered, "I'll try that."

So Rocky came over to our yard and ate all the grass under the shrubs that I couldn't mow. When he finished, he called me to come over and see what he had done.

Somewhat surprised by the good job he did, I said, "You did a fantastic job here today, Rocky. Thank you so much."

Rocky beamed from ear to ear and said, "You know, I feel really good about the work I did."

I said, "My grandmother used to say, 'Many hands make light work.' Now I can't wait to go back to church and tell the boys and girls about your wonderful help. Maybe they will start helping their families around the house, as well as their church and school."

"Your grandmother was right," Rocky said, "but from now on, we'll have to say, 'Many *paws* make light work!'"

Scripture verse: "How long will you lie there, O lazybones? When will you rise from your sleep?" (Prov. 6:7).

Rocky Wants to Be a Better Bear

When I visited Rocky yesterday, he was reading his Bible. I said, "Rocky, I'm glad to see you reading your Bible today."

Rocky said, "All those boys and girls at the church seem to know so much about the Bible. I need to study it a lot more."

"We can never know as much about the Bible as we would like to know," I replied. "And it's not how much we know about it that matters most to God. It's really whether we let the Bible help us grow. It doesn't do us much good if we know all the stories, yet don't live by them."

"You hit the nail on the head, Dr. Bob," Rocky said, putting his Bible down on the lake bank. "I was just reading about all these things the Bible says we should be doing, and I began to feel bad."

"How so, Rocky?" I asked.

"Well," said Rocky, "I read that we ought to love others no matter what they do to us. You know how hard it is for me to love Robert Rabbit. He makes me so mad that I can't tell a blueberry from a strawberry!"

"I know what you mean, Rocky," I said. "Sometimes

others make us really mad. But God wants us to keep on hoping they will change. God wants us to keep on wishing the best for them."

But Rocky was clearly upset. He said, "And I read here in the Bible that I'm supposed to be faithful. My, oh my, just this morning I promised to meet Amy Aardvark to show her where the anthills are around here. But then I decided to go swimming and left her waiting at the dock."

"Many before you have said the same thing, Rocky," I told him. "Those great people in the Bible like Moses and Peter felt like giving up on themselves sometimes. But God gave them another chance. And God gives us another chance, too."

"But," Rocky said, "I don't have much self-control. Instead of just eating one or two of your blueberries, I have to eat every last one of them!"

"Once again," I said, "just when you feel like giving up on yourself, God says, 'I still love you. I forgive you and will help you.'"

"That gives me hope," Rocky said. "I'm glad to know that God doesn't give up on us but always gives us another chance."

Scripture verse: "But be doers of the word, and not merely hearers who deceive themselves" (Jas. 1:22).

Rocky Becomes a Steward

Yesterday I greeted Rocky by saying, "What's happening, my friend?"

"Oh," said Rocky, "I have some exciting plans. Ramola has invited me to go on a picnic tomorrow and has even invited Amy Aardvark to go, too."

"Sounds like fun," I said. "I know that Amy will fix some delicious termite sandwiches and serve red ant ice cream for dessert! When are you going?"

"Tomorrow at 11 o'clock," Rocky said, "so don't pick me up for church."

"But, Rocky," I replied, "you always go to church with Gail and me."

"I know I do," Rocky said, "but all I do is sit there in my bear suit and stare at the boys and girls. Still, maybe we can have the picnic today instead."

"I'm glad you're going with us," I said. Later I went back to ask how the picnic went.

"Great!" Rocky replied. "The food was wonderful. It was so peaceful sitting by the lake. Even those termite sandwiches were better than I expected!"

"But Rocky," I asked, "what's all that stuff floating around in the lake?"

"Oh, that's just our picnic trash," Rocky said. "When we finished, we took everything and threw it in the lake. It'll float away when the wind blows."

"I can't believe you said that, Rocky," I replied. "God wants us to be good stewards and take care of the earth."

"What's a steward?" Rocky asked. "I've never heard of a steward before!"

"A steward takes care of something for someone else," I replied. "We are God's stewards, and God wants us to take care of the earth God gave us."

Rocky looked at me as if a light bulb had turned on. "I guess we didn't take care of God's earth when we threw all that trash in the lake," he said.

"*You* said it, Rocky!" I answered. "Now let's get all your friends together and have a little talk about taking care of things around this lot." So that's what we did.

Rocky and his friends learned to be good stewards yesterday. The last time I saw them they were walking around the vacant lot picking up trash!

Scripture verse: "The earth is the Lord's and all that is in it . . ." (Ps. 24:1a).

Rocky Is Jealous

Rocky hardly noticed me yesterday when I visited him. "What's happening, Rocky?" I asked, sitting down by him under a pine tree.

"You don't want to know, Dr. Bob," Rocky replied.

"Try me," I said, "maybe I *do* want to know."

"Okay," said Rocky. "I'm jealous of Daniel Duck. Everybody is always talking about how great he is."

"And that bothers you a lot to hear others praise him?" I asked.

"Of course it does!" Rocky said. "I want them to talk about me and say how great I am. Why, I've had mountains named after me . . . the *Rocky* Mountains. Football teams, too . . . the Chicago *Bears*. And even baseball teams . . . the Chicago *Cubs.*

"I don't want to hear any more about that stupid duck. I'm sick of him getting all the attention. I'm even tired of hearing him say, 'Quack, quack,' all the time."

"What do you do when you feel jealous of Daniel?" I asked.

"Oh," said Rocky, "I've been thinking about how I can cut him down by saying, 'He can't fish the way I can. He can't run as fast as I can.'"

"But do you think that will help you?" I asked.

Rocky said, "Sure, it will work. They will notice *me*, not *him*!"

"Yes," I quickly replied, "they will notice how jealous you are. And they will like Daniel even more."

"Uh, oh," moaned Rocky. "What should I do then?"

"Good question, Rocky," I replied. "Think about why Daniel is so well-liked. Realize that he really is an outstanding duck. Just don't try to cut him down. Then look at yourself and think about all the gifts God has given you. You can just be yourself. We need Daniel around here, but we also need you. There's a place for both of you!"

"Thanks, Dr. Bob," Rocky said. "I'll try, but it's hard to do." About that time Daniel swam by. Rocky wished him a nice day.

And Daniel said, "It would be even nicer if you would come and swim with me!" They swam together happily the rest of the afternoon.

Scripture verse: "Love doesn't want what it doesn't have ..." (1 Cor. 13:4, Msg.).

Rocky Has a Worry

When I walked toward Rocky's cave yesterday, I heard a loud noise. It sounded as if someone was sawing wood. I was afraid a tree might fall on our house! But to my surprise I saw Rocky lying on the ground and snoring his furry head off. He was making as much noise as a chain saw! When he heard me walking on the dry leaves, he woke up with a start.

"My, Rocky," I said, "you're sleeping late today. Or are you already taking a nap?"

"Yes," Rocky said, "I am sleeping late today."

"Have you been eating my blueberries again?" I asked.

"Oh, no," Rocky replied quickly. "I was scared by the loud noises I heard all night long. Boom! Boom! Boom! I looked over at your house, but all the lights were off. And that scared me even more. I haven't been that scared since I left the mountains."

"I'm so sorry you were scared," I said. "God is always with us whether it is light or dark. God made both of them."

"I guess I knew that," Rocky said, "but I still don't like the dark. I get scared. Everything seems worse at night. But what *were* those noises?"

"Those booms you heard," I said, "came from Fort

Bragg. Our soldiers were firing their big guns, practicing in the night. They want to keep us safe."

"Oh, I see," Rocky said. "It helps a lot to know the reason for the noise."

"Good," I told him. "And next time, I hope you'll knock on our door when you get scared. It helps to be with friends when you are afraid. Our friends and families are God's helpers who make us feel better."

"Okay," Rocky replied, "I'll be sure to knock on your door the next time I get scared."

"Now, Rocky," I said, "don't forget to do that. Gail might even give you a slice of her blueberry pie! And even though you can't see God, remember that God loves you. God is with you at all times, in the dark and in the light, when you are afraid, and when you are not afraid. Count on it."

Scripture verse: "The Lord is my light and my salvation; whom shall I fear?" (Ps. 27:1a).

Rocky Throws a Party

Rocky was writing names on a list yesterday . . . Ramola Bear, Robert Rabbit, Daniel Duck, Amy Aardvark . . .

"What are those names you have there on your list, Rocky?" I asked.

"I'm still sort of new around here," Rocky replied. "I might have a party and make better friends with some of the animals. What do you think?"

"Good idea," I said, looking at the list. "Hmm," I added, "I notice that you left out Roberta Rabbit, Robert's younger sister."

"Right!" Rocky exclaimed. "She's really stuck on herself. She looks at herself in the lake every day."

"Maybe you should include her anyway," I said. "Perhaps she needs a friend, too. By the way, what will you serve at your party?"

"Oh, I'll just serve water from the lake," Rocky answered.

"Lake water?" I asked, somewhat surprised. "But I guess they'll like that, especially Daniel Duck. And what else?"

"Popcorn!" Rocky said.

"Popcorn?" I asked. "Bears don't eat popcorn."

"Oh, yes," Rocky said. "One night you and Gail were eating popcorn on your deck. Both of you went inside for a minute. That hot popcorn smelled so good that I reached over the railing and ate a pawful."

"You ate more than a pawful!" I said, laughing. "Now I know what happened to that big bowl of popcorn."

Later on Rocky had his party. Coming to church today I asked him, "How did your party go?"

"Not too well," Rocky said. "The popcorn just didn't taste right."

"Did you put any salt on it?" I asked.

"Salt?" Rocky replied. "I didn't know I was supposed to put salt on it."

"A little salt makes popcorn taste just right," I said. "Jesus said we are like salt. When we do good things for others, we make life better for them just as salt makes popcorn taste better."

"Next time I'll remember that," said Rocky, "and the salt, too!"

Scripture verse: "You are the salt of the earth . . ." (Matt. 5:13a).

Rocky Gives Thanks

I found Rocky snacking on my blueberries again yesterday, but I didn't say anything about it. "What's going on, Rocky, my man?" I asked.

"Not much," Rocky answered. "I was just thinking about my friend Daniel Duck. He's always doing something nice for somebody. Do you remember when Robert Rabbit got a thorn in his paw?"

"I sure do," I replied. "He cried and cried."

"Well," Rocky said, "Daniel found some of those healing weeds in the lake and put them on Robert's paw. His paw felt better in a few minutes."

"And what did Robert say?" I asked.

"Nothing," Rocky replied, "absolutely nothing. He just hopped on off. And do you remember Billy Squirrel?"

"Oh, yes," I said, "how could I forget that little rascal who cleans out my bird feeder every day?"

Rocky said, "One day Billy was hanging from a limb over the lake when he suddenly dropped his acorn. Daniel saw it floating around in the lake. So he swam over and got it, and took it to Billy on the bank."

"And what did Billy say?" I asked.

"Nothing," Rocky replied, "absolutely nothing."

"I'm sorry Robert and Billy haven't learned to say thank you," I said.

"I am, too!" Rocky said. "Then when I saw Billy having fun swinging over the lake, I decided to try it, too. I climbed a tree, but the limb broke and I plopped into the lake. All the animals except Daniel laughed and laughed. But Daniel swam over and said, 'Hey, Rocky, let's swim over to the other side of the lake.' And we did."

"What did you tell Daniel?" I asked.

"Thank you, thank you!" Rocky said, "Thank you for being my friend at all times, even when others are laughing at me."

"Rocky," I said, "that's great that you thanked Daniel. But I'm still waiting for you to thank *me* for all those blueberries you ate! After all, this is the Thanksgiving season."

Scripture verse: "Praise the Lord! O give thanks to the Lord, for he is good" (Ps. 106:1a).

Rocky and the Shoe Box

I didn't have to go over to see Rocky yesterday because he was sitting on our deck. "You're up bright and early this morning, Rocky," I said.

"Yes, I am, Dr. Bob," Rocky replied, "Gail asked me to come over and watch her pack a Christmas shoe box with gifts. And, to tell you the truth, I thought there might be a gift lying around for me!"

"Now I get it, Rocky," I said. "I knew that there must be a good reason for you to be up so early on Saturday morning!"

"Where is the shoe box?" Rocky asked.

Gail came out with the shoe box jammed full of presents for poor children in another country.

"That little box won't do any good," Rocky sniffed. "It would hardly hold a basket of blueberries!"

Gail said, "Rocky, the children who'll get these presents don't usually get anything for Christmas."

"Why not?" Rocky asked. "Have they been bad?"

"Oh, no," Gail said, "their parents are poor and just don't have any money."

"Hmm," said Rocky, peering into the box, "I thought *everybody* had enough money." Then Rocky saw a toothbrush in the box and asked Gail why she had bought it.

"Well," Gail said, "some children have never had a toothbrush before. That's why we also have to send them toothpaste and explain how to brush teeth."

Rocky just sat there, thinking. A light bulb went on, and he said, "It looks like even that won't do much good unless we keep sending them money to buy more toothpaste. We need to send them a dentist, too."

"Good thinking, Rocky," Gail said. "A dentist in our church does go for two weeks every year. She's teaching the children how to brush their teeth."

With his big paws Rocky started looking through the box. He pulled out a little truck, a yo-yo, and some crayons. Then he said, "I'm glad you're sending the children the shoe box for Christmas. Now, do you have any gifts for me?"

"Oh, yes," Gail and I laughed, "a whole wheelbarrow full!"

Scripture verse: "How does God's love abide in anyone who has the world's goods and sees a brother or sister in need and yet refuses to help?" (1 John 3:17).

Rocky Learns a Lesson

Yesterday I didn't have to look hard for Rocky. I heard him banging some tree limbs on my dock down at the lake.

"Rocky," I shouted, "why all the loud noise?"

"I want the other animals to hear me and gather 'round," Rocky said.

"What on earth for?" I asked.

"Oh," said Rocky, "Daniel Duck has been sick for a week. I want to take him some tea and blueberries to help him feel better."

"That's a really nice thing to do, Rocky," I said, "but why all the noise?"

"Well," said Rocky, "I want everybody to see me give Daniel the tea and blueberries so they will think I'm a wonderful bear!"

"Rocky," I said, "maybe God doesn't want us to run around trying to get credit for everything we do."

"Why would you say such a thing, Dr. Bob?" Rocky asked. "I *like* to get credit for everything I do!"

"I think we all do, Rocky," I admitted. "If you work hard to make the honor roll in school, you like to see your name in the paper. But Jesus said we shouldn't make such a big deal out of helping others. He said we should do it in secret, and then God would reward us."

"But I still like to get credit for everything *I* do," Rocky shot back.

"I guess," I said, "it's just a matter of who gives us the credit . . . others or God. Suppose a little boy in eastern Europe is cold today, and we send him a blanket to keep him warm. That little boy will never know our name, but God does. And God will always reward us by blessing us in some way. So we don't have to show off to others all the time. We give others blankets to help them stay warm, not because we need for them to give us high fives."

Suddenly Rocky put his tree limb down. "Why were you making such a racket, Rocky?" asked Robert Rabbit, who was scurrying by.

"Never mind, it wasn't important," Rocky said as he headed for Daniel's house with tea and blueberries. He didn't say a word to anybody!

Scripture verse: "Be especially careful when you are trying to be good so that you don't make a performance out of it" (Matt. 6:1, Msg.).

Rocky Gives a Christmas Present

Once again I didn't have to look for Rocky yesterday. Instead, he came running over to our house and almost knocked the front door down.

"My," I said, "you're excited today. What's going on?"

"Dr. Bob," Rocky replied, "please tell me how you people make all the money you spend on Christmas presents every year."

"Okay, Rocky," I answered, "but why would you want to know that? Aren't you happy just climbing trees and playing with Ramola?"

"Well," Rocky said, "I'm happy enough, but I want to make enough money to buy you a present like a sport utility vehicle. Then everybody will think I have a lot of money and am a big spender!"

"But, Rocky," I said, "that's not the reason we give to each other."

"All right," Rocky replied, "I'll give you a new DVD player. You'll be so busy watching a movie that you won't notice me when I eat your blueberries!"

"Again, Rocky," I said, "that's not why we give gifts to each other."

"Okay," Rocky said, "I'll just give you a new suit because I feel guilty for eating all your blueberries!"

"But that's not why we give to each other either," I said.

"Guess I have a lot of thinking to do about why we give presents," Rocky said, running off through the woods.

Early this morning Rocky came back, holding a small box in his hand. "Here's a puny little present, Dr. Bob," Rocky said. "It's not much, but I just wanted to thank you for our friendship."

"That was kind of you, Rocky," I said, opening the box. Inside was a bottle of honey shaped like a little bear.

"Thank you, Rocky!" I said. "This is a wonderful gift. Every time I put honey on my waffles it will remind me of our friendship. And here is your gift."

Rocky opened the box I handed him. Inside was a new Bible. "Awesome!" Rocky said. "Now I can read about Jesus, God's great gift to us."

Scripture verse: "For God so loved the world that he gave his only Son, so that everyone who believes in him may not perish but may have eternal life" (John 3:16).

Rocky Wants Christmas to Come Back

Yesterday Rocky told me he had a big Christmas. "I was pleased," he bragged, "that so many people remembered me." Still, he looked sad.

"So what's wrong, Rocky?" I asked, surprised that he seemed sad.

"Oh, Dr. Bob," he replied, "Christmas just flew by! I got lots of cards and gifts . . . steaks, Blueberry Morning cereal, and a new bear suit. But now I have to wait a whole year before Christmas comes again. A whole year!"

"I feel the same way," I replied. "I can't wait until Christmas comes, and then it goes by so fast. But I have found something that helps me now."

"And what's that, Dr. Bob?" Rocky asked. "I'd like to know your secret."

"Well," I said, "you gave me a jar of honey, and I loved it. That made me happy. Then I gave each boy and girl in the church a jar of honey. I hope that made them happy."

"Yes, I remember that," Rocky said.

"Okay," I continued, "at Christmas we think about God's love because he gave us his son Jesus. And we have given each other gifts. It's such fun to open a gift and to think that somebody cared enough about us to give us a present. We don't have to wait until Christmas to do that again."

"But," said Rocky, "if I keep giving gifts until next Christmas, I'll be broke!"

"Yes," I chuckled, "I guess you would be. But you can give others a big smile. That's a gift. And you can tell others you're sorry when things go wrong between you. That's a special gift. Those gifts will make every day seem like Christmas to them."

"But what about *me*?" Rocky replied. "I want some presents, too!"

"I know you do," I laughed. "And yet, others give us gifts all the time . . . gifts of food, gifts of smiles, and gifts of friendship."

"Yes, yes," Rocky said impatiently, "but I like *bear* toys."

"I'll bet you do," I said, "but to make every day seem like Christmas, try to give someone else a gift by doing something good for them. It will make a big difference in their life. And yours, too!"

Scripture verse: "Give and it will be given to you. A good measure, pressed down, shaken together, running over will be put into your lap . . ." (Luke 6:38a).

Rocky Is Tempted

"Rocky," I asked yesterday when I saw him, "what was going on over here a minute ago? I heard a loud splash in the lake and much growling."

"Oh, Dr. Bob," Rocky began, "I was hoping you didn't see or hear us. My day got off to a 'rocky' start."

"What happened?" I asked. "I thought everything would be going just great around the ole barnyard here. After all, it's the Christmas season, a time of love, joy, and peace."

"Well," Rocky answered, "I'll tell you what happened, but I really don't like to talk about it. Robert Rabbit was strutting around in his new rabbit suit on Christmas Day. He kept looking at himself in the lake and saying how good looking he was. And then he said, 'Not only am I good looking, but I'm the fastest runner around here, too.' He kept on bragging. The more he bragged, the more I wanted to push him right into the lake."

"But surely you didn't do it, Rocky," I said. "That water is cold, almost cold enough to freeze."

"Yes, I did," Rocky said, lowering his head. "That was the loud splash you heard. I pushed him right in. I had heard enough from that big mouth. He came up out of the lake soaking wet and very cold. Then he ran off through the woods and crawled into his hole in the ground."

"How are you feeling now?" I asked. "I know Robert must be cold and mad."

"Yes," Rocky said, "and I feel terrible about what I did. When I think about doing a bad thing, I just have to find a way not to do it. But every time it seems that I do it anyway. What will help me?"

"Good question, Rocky," I replied. "When I'm tempted to do something I know is wrong, I start thinking about something else. It helps me to think about Jesus. Jesus was tempted too, but he didn't do anything wrong. It also helps to think about some of our good church members. I don't think they would give in to the desire to hurt someone."

"Now I feel so guilty for what I did!" Rocky said.

"Remember, Rocky," I said, "not only does Jesus help us when we are tempted, but he also forgives us when we do wrong. And that's good news!"

Scripture verse: "Because he himself was tested by what he suffered, he is able to help those who are being tested" (Heb. 2:18).

Rocky Has Surgery

I noticed yesterday that Rocky's stuffing was coming out! Gail said, "For goodness sake! Rocky will have to have surgery."

At once I said, "Let's call Grace McGill, our friend in Aberdeen, who sews. She can do the surgery by putting new stuffing in Rocky and sewing him back up."

Grace said, "I'll be glad to fix Rocky for you." So one night I took him to her house and left him for his operation.

I hadn't been home five minutes before I got a call from Rocky on his cell phone. "Dr. Bob," he began, "I'm scared again!"

"What scares you the most, Rocky?" I asked.

Rocky said, "I'm afraid the stitches will hurt and that I won't heal quickly."

"Oh, Rocky," I said cheerfully, "you've always eaten a good diet of blueberries, fish, and nuts. I suspect you'll heal just fine."

"I'm lonely, too," Rocky said. I could tell he didn't want to stop talking.

"We're all praying for you, Rocky," I replied. "Try repeating this verse: 'The Lord is the stronghold of my life; of whom shall I be afraid?'"

"Thank you, Dr. Bob," Rocky said. "I'll remember that."

About noon the next day Grace called and said, "You can come by and pick up Rocky any time you wish."

"Good," I answered. "And how did his surgery go?"

"Fine!" Grace replied. "He's as good as new."

When Rocky got home, we showed him all the cards and letters he got from his church friends. He even received two e-cards. "When I was afraid," he said, "it really helped me to know that the church was praying for me."

"The church always helps us when we're scared," I said.

"It also helped me to remember that God was with me, too," Rocky said. "Over and over again I said that Bible verse, 'The Lord is the stronghold of my life; of whom shall I be afraid?' And it worked!"

Scripture verse: "The Lord is the stronghold of my life; of whom shall I be afraid?" (Ps. 27:1b).

Rocky Adds on More Land

Yesterday I saw Rocky tying ribbons around many of the trees on the vacant lot. "What are you doing, Rocky?" I called out.

"Oh," Rocky replied, "I'm tying these red ribbons around everything I want around here!"

"But you have even tied one around *my* favorite blueberry bush," I said. "And you've put one on Robert Rabbit's home. Why, why?"

"I'm just branching out," Rocky replied. "I'm taking more land. You told me about Jabez, that man in the Bible who wanted God to give him more land."

"But, Rocky," I said, "that didn't mean that God would let him take over everybody else's land, too!"

"Hmm," Rocky answered, "I always thought God would give you anything you prayed for!"

"No, no," I said. "The world would really be in a mess if we could simply ask God for anything and get it. When we ask God for more, we should ask God to show us what he wants us to have and to do. And surely God wants us to be more helpful to others. God likes that kind of prayer!"

"Guess I really didn't understand that Bible story!" Rocky replied.

The last time I saw Rocky yesterday, he was taking all the ribbons off of my blueberry bushes. Then he marched over and pulled the ribbon off of Robert's home as well. One by one he untied all the ribbons.

Then Rocky yelled to all his friends in a loud voice, "Hey, everyone! Come to a party at my cave at five o'clock this afternoon."

"Rocky," I asked, "what are you doing now? You have untied all your ribbons and are giving a party for your friends."

"Well, Dr. Bob," he replied, "you said that when we ask God for more, we should ask him to show us how to become more helpful. So I thought I would share more with my friends. At the party I'm also going to ask my friends how we can make this a better place to live."

"Wonderful, Rocky!" I said. "My, when you get a new idea, you really know how to put it to work."

Scripture verse: "Jabez called on the God of Israel, saying, 'Oh that you would bless me and enlarge my border ...'" (1 Chr. 4:10a).

Rocky Is Lonely

Rocky was sitting by a pine tree yesterday, eating a peanut butter and honey sandwich. "How's it going, Rocky?" I asked when I saw him.

"Not so well," Rocky replied. "You know Ramola Bear, don't you?"

"Oh, yes," I said. "How could I ever forget Ramola? My grandchildren in Georgia gave her to us to be your special friend."

"That's just the problem," Rocky said. "She *used* to be my friend, but no more. We had a big fuss. Now I don't want to play with her anymore."

"So how about Daniel Duck?" I asked, trying to be helpful. "There's never been a better friend to anyone than Daniel."

"I know that," Rocky answered. "But Daniel said he had to look for a special weed that ducks like to eat."

"And so," I said, "I can see why you're feeling sort of lonely today."

"That's right," Rocky said. "And I can't play with you. You don't like to play bear games. You don't climb trees. You don't like to eat blue . . ." Rocky caught himself. He was about to say *blueberries.*

"Yes," I replied quickly. "I *do* like blueberries, Rocky. Only I can never find any blueberries on my bushes.

You have eaten them all!"

Rocky grinned and said, "You nailed me there, Dr. Bob! Where can we find blueberries these days?"

"I know someone in Cameron who grows blueberries," I replied. "Let's go over there." So we went to Cameron and bought some blueberries.

Coming home, Rocky said, "Thanks for going with me, Dr. Bob. I don't feel quite as lonely anymore."

"I had a good time, too, Rocky," I said. "Friends always help us when we feel lonely. Now, how about making up with Ramola? Let's go find her. I know where her cave is."

In a few minutes Rocky and Ramola were shaking paws and making up. What a delight to see them playing together again!

Scripture verse: "Live in harmony with one another . . ." (Rom. 12:16a).

Rocky Doesn't Want to Go to Church

Yesterday Rocky was sitting under a pine tree, looking at the lake. "You seem to be thinking a lot this morning, Rocky," I said.

"Yes, yes, Dr. Bob," Rocky replied. "I was thinking that I don't want to go to church with you tomorrow."

"That's strange, Rocky," I said. "We're going to Jackson Springs Presbyterian Church, so you know we'll have a good time. We'll meet some new boys and girls."

"That's just it," Rocky replied. "You drag me around everywhere you go . . . Vass, Carthage, Aberdeen, Southern Pines, Hamlet, and Pinehurst. I sit there in front of the church and stare at the boys and girls!"

"C'mon, Rocky," I said, "you're always telling me how much fun you had at those churches and how many friends you made."

"I guess you're right," Rocky replied. "But I'm always a little shy at first about meeting new boys and girls. I'm afraid they won't like my bear suit. I'm afraid they will laugh at me because I sleep a lot. I'm really afraid they won't like me, period."

"And Rocky," I said. "I wonder about a *lot* of things when I meet new people, too. I wonder whether they will like my grown-up sermons and my children's sermons. I even wonder if they will like me."

Rocky replied, "So what can I do about it?"

"Just be yourself," I said. "Talk to the boys and girls. Ask them how they are doing. If they go to school, ask them how school is going. Usually when you take an interest in others, they will take an interest in you. You will make many new friends at Jackson Springs, too. The church is God's special house and God's special people. The church is where we can love and be loved."

Then I told the boys and girls at church that I wanted Rocky to be their special friend for a few weeks. I also asked them to bring one of their special stuffed friends to church.

The very next Sunday Rocky could hardly believe it. Every boy and girl brought a teddy bear to church! Already he had made many new friends.

"And just think," Rocky said on the way home, "not long ago I didn't want to go to church. Now I can't wait until next Sunday!"

Scripture verse: "I was glad when they said to me, 'Let us go to the house of the Lord'" (Ps. 122:1).

Rocky Wants to Be the Greatest

Rocky was lying on the lake bank yesterday, snoozing away in the early morning sun. There was a blue ring around his mouth. I knew he had been eating my blueberries again. I asked, "What's up, Rocky?"

Slowly Rocky got to his feet and said, "Oh, I was just thinking important thoughts today."

"I'll bet you were," I replied. "You were thinking about how you can eat more of my blueberries!"

"No, no!" Rocky said, "I'm thinking about who is the greatest animal around here."

"And what have you decided, Rocky?" I asked. "Who is the greatest?"

"At first I thought it was Robert Rabbit," Rocky said. "He runs so fast and hops faster than anyone else. He's amazing."

"Then I thought it was Billy Squirrel," Rocky continued. "He can jump from limb to limb and run up and down trees quicker than any animal I know."

"Next," Rocky said, "I figured it was Daniel Duck. He can swim better and dive deeper than anyone I have ever seen."

"So what did you finally decide, Rocky?" I asked, holding my breath. "Who is the greatest creature around here?"

Rocky paused a moment and said, "I decided that Daniel Duck was the greatest, but not because he can swim so fast and dive so deep. No, he's the greatest because he tries to be a helpful friend to everyone.

"When my paw was sore, he put a special weed on it, and it got well. When Billy dropped his acorn in the lake, Daniel swam over and got it for him. Daniel is a friend to all of us. That's why he's the greatest."

"Good thinking, Rocky," I replied. "You *did* have an important thought. In fact, Jesus himself once said that the greatest among us is the one who serves, the one who is loving and kind. Not everyone can run or swim fast or be the smartest. But everyone of us can be kind and helpful."

And Rocky said, "I'm glad we had this talk today, Dr. Bob. And now, sir, would you be so kind and helpful as to bring me some more of your blueberries!?"

Scripture verse: "... whoever wishes to be great among you must be your servant" (Mark 10:43b).

Rocky Lets His Friends Down

"Why are you so happy today?" I asked Rocky yesterday.

"Oh, Dr. Bob," Rocky said, "today is my birthday, and all my friends are giving me a birthday party. Let's talk this afternoon after the party."

I went back to see Rocky about 4 o'clock. I could tell he had been crying. I said, "Rocky, it's your birthday. Cheer up!"

After wiping away his tears, Rocky said, "The party was supposed to be at 1 o'clock. But Ramola Bear came by about noon and invited me to go fishing. You know how we bears like to scoop up fish with our paws."

"Yes," I said, "but surely you didn't miss your own birthday party!"

"Well," Rocky said, "I did leave them a sign in front of my cave. I told them I had decided to go fishing. But they didn't like it very much. Robert Rabbit left a note telling me to go jump in the lake. He said he had brought me a carrot, but that he would just eat it himself."

"Sounds as though he was pretty angry," I said.

"So was Amy Aardvark," Rocky replied. "She left a note saying she had bought me a jar of termite jelly but that she was going to eat it herself."

"This is so sad, Rocky!" I said.

"I guess I let every friend down," Rocky said. "And they were trying to do such nice things for me, too. But I do have one friend left."

"Who's that?" I asked, wondering who would still be his friend.

"Daniel Duck, that's who," Rocky replied. "He brought me a blueberry pie. His note said, 'Happy Birthday, Rocky. You'll always be my special friend.'"

"Unbelievable," I said. "In other words, Daniel still wanted you to have the present even though you let him and everybody else down. That sounds like the way Jesus was with his friend, a disciple named Peter. When Peter let Jesus down, Jesus kept on loving him. And that's the way Jesus is with us."

"I'm glad you told me about Jesus' friend Peter, Dr. Bob," Rocky said. "It helps me to know that Jesus loves us the same way."

Scripture verse: "A friend loves at all times" (Prov. 17:17a).

Rocky Faces Himself

Yesterday Rocky pushed Robert Rabbit into the lake again. He seemed so pleased with himself, but I couldn't understand it.

"Oh, Dr. Bob," Rocky said, "I did a good thing. Every animal loved it except Robert!"

"Rocky," I said, "let's talk about your troubles with Robert Rabbit. Maybe those little fusses you two have are not all Robert's fault."

"How could you say such a thing?" Rocky asked. "All the animals know that Robert is 100% wrong and that I'm 100% right."

"Well," I said, "sometimes we all do things that make it hard for others to get along with us. And we don't even realize it."

"I know myself very well, Dr. Bob," Rocky said. "What can *you* tell me that I don't already know?"

"Rocky," I replied, "we are just not able to see ourselves the way others see us. Often they have to tell us things we need to hear."

"Go ahead, now," Rocky said, looking me right in the eye, "tell me one thing about myself that I don't already know."

"Well," I said, trying to be gentle, "some of the animals tell me you like to throw your weight around.

You growl at them as if you're going to beat 'em up. That scares little animals like Robert Rabbit."

"You must be kidding me, Dr. Bob," Rocky said. "I growl only when I get scared. Nobody around here really thinks I'm dangerous."

"But that's just what I'm saying, Rocky," I replied. "Other animals have told me again and again that you scare them with those fierce growls of yours."

After a long pause Rocky said, "If it is true, what can I do about it?"

I said, "Ask God and your friends to help you see yourself more clearly. God wants us to grow, and one way we grow is to understand ourselves better."

"Thanks for helping me," Rocky answered. "Now, do you want me to tell you something about yourself that you don't know?"

"I guess so, Rocky," I replied, somewhat surprised.

"Well," Rocky said with a twinkle in his big eyes, "I didn't want to say it, but you love to talk. Every time I see you in church you're talking!"

Scripture verse: "Why do you see the speck in your neighbor's eye, but do not notice the log in your own eye?" (Matt. 7:3).

Rocky Counts the Cost

Rocky came running up to me yesterday as I approached. "Daniel Duck," he said, "told me that they are having the Animal Olympics soon. I've been thinking about entering three contests."

"And what are those contests?" I asked.

"Well," Rocky replied, "I didn't want to do swimming, because I'm just learning to swim. I might get tired and have to yell for help."

"I can see why you're not swimming," I said. "Besides, Daniel Duck has that event sewed up. He can swim very fast . . . long distances, too."

"Then I thought about tree climbing," Rocky said. "But I knew that nobody had a chance against Billy Squirrel. He's the fastest ever."

"I see," I said. "What about running through the briars then?"

"That didn't appeal to me either," Rocky said. "The other day I ran through the briars and got one stuck in my paw and had to go to the doctor. Not one of those things was worth doing. Each one would cost too much."

"I don't blame you for counting the cost of taking part in the contests, Rocky," I said. "Jesus once said we ought to count the cost when we do things. So are you going to take part in the Olympics at all?"

"Yes," said Rocky, "I am going to enter the *blueberry eating contest.*"

"You'll win that," I said, "but even as good as you are, you'll have to practice a lot. You're not the only animal that likes blueberries!"

"Maybe I can practice on *your* blueberry bushes, Dr. Bob!" Rocky said.

"You've been doing that for a long time!" I laughed. "But I might let you practice a little when my blueberries get ripe. 'Practice makes perfect,' I've always heard."

So Rocky practiced eating blueberries. Then he won a gold medal in the blueberry eating contest! But he did something even better. Some of the animals wouldn't play with Mike Muskrat because he was new. Rocky knew the other animals would tease him if he played with Mike. But he did it anyway. He counted the cost and did what was right. And later he was glad he did.

"Rocky," I said, "winning the blueberry contest was exciting. But it was even more exciting to see you do what was right by playing with Mike."

Scripture verse: "For which of you, intending to build a tower, does not first sit down and estimate the cost, to see whether he has enough to complete it?" (Luke 14:28).

Rocky Waves a Palm Branch

Yesterday when I saw Rocky he was reading his Bible. Putting his Bible down, Rocky seemed eager to talk.

"Dr. Bob," he began, "I've been reading about Palm Sunday. It was interesting that Jesus rode into Jerusalem on a donkey. I've never liked donkeys too much . . . they kick a lot! The people really seemed to be happy. They were shouting and waving palm branches. What a welcome Jesus received!"

"That's right, Rocky," I said, "they seemed so happy on Sunday. But by Friday everything changed. Some of those same people who cheered him on Sunday were yelling against him on Friday. In just a few short days, everything changed."

"Unbelievable!" Rocky said. "How could they change so fast?"

"I've wondered about that, too," I replied. "But then one day I asked myself, 'Don't all of us do the same thing?'"

"Oh, I don't think so, Dr. Bob," Rocky said. "And I think that if Jesus came back today, we would welcome him gladly."

"I certainly hope so," I said, "but I'm not sure we would. We are really no different from those people on Palm Sunday."

"What do you mean?" Rocky asked.

"Well," I said, "some days we like each other but then, on other days, we don't like each other very much. We quickly change."

"Oh," Rocky said, "I see what you mean. One day I like Robert Rabbit, and we run through the woods together. But the next day he makes me very mad, and I want to push him into the lake. I guess I change, too!"

"But, Rocky," I said, "one thing doesn't change, and that is God. God keeps on loving us on Sunday, Monday, and Tuesday. Even when we displease God, God keeps on loving us."

And Rocky said, "The next time I wave a palm branch on Sunday, I'll try to remember God's love that never changes!"

Scripture verse: "Jesus Christ is the same yesterday and today and forever" (Heb. 13:8).

Rocky and Easter Sunday

Rocky was waiting for me yesterday when I visited him. He said a couple of things were bothering him. "Why didn't you plan to take me on the Easter egg hunt at the church today?" he began.

"Oh, my goodness," I said. "I didn't think bears liked Easter egg hunts."

"We do, too," Rocky said. "That shows how little you know about us bears sometimes. We use big ostrich eggs instead of chicken eggs for our hunts!"

"But what else is bothering you?" I asked. "You said there was another thing."

"Yes," Rocky replied. "Daniel Duck and his family have flown back to Canada for the summer."

"How do you know that?" I asked.

"Well, this morning," Rocky said, "I heard the ducks quacking and quacking all over the place. Then they flew up into the air and took off together. I just know they have gone and left us forever. And Daniel was my best friend. He even took up for me when I broke my promise by not staying home for my own birthday party. What will I ever do without Daniel?"

"I can see why you are so unhappy," I said, looking toward the northern sky. In the distance I could see what seemed to be some birds flying together. They got closer and closer, circled back over the lake, and then landed a few feet from us. Daniel and his family were back!

Rocky ran to the water's edge to meet Daniel and said, "Daniel, I thought you had flown away for the summer!"

"No, no," Daniel said. "We just flew over to a beautiful pond at the Bethesda Church in Aberdeen. We heard there were some delicious weeds over there to eat. We won't be flying to Canada for a few weeks yet."

"I'm glad that Daniel and his family are back," I said. "This reminds me of the way Jesus' friends once felt. They thought he had died and that they would never see him again. They were very sad. But on Easter Jesus appeared to them again. They were so happy. They knew he would always be with them. And so, Rocky, that's good news for us, too. Jesus is alive and will always be with us."

Scripture verse: "And remember, I am with you always, to the close of the age" (Matt. 28:20b).

Rocky and Grandpa Bear

Rocky was sitting under his favorite pine tree yesterday. But his head was down, and he was staring at the lake. I noticed a tear rolling down his face.

When Rocky saw me coming, he quickly wiped the tear away and said, "Dr. Bob, you told me I should be happy living in God's beautiful world with my friends."

"Yes, yes," I replied, "so why are you crying?"

"Well," said Rocky, "last night I called Mama Bear in the mountains on my cell phone. Grandpa Bear didn't come to the phone, and he always does. I asked Mama where he was, and she said I wouldn't see him anymore on this earth.

"Then I remembered that the last time I talked to him, he could hardly growl. Also, the last time I saw him, his fur was falling out. From what Mama Bear said, I don't think Grandpa Bear is alive anymore."

"Oh, Rocky," I said, putting my hand on his furry back, "I'm so sorry. Of course, it's right to be sad at such a time—and to shed some tears. Tell me what's going on."

"Well," Rocky said, "My girlfriend Ramola and I are collecting pictures of Grandpa Bear to put in a scrapbook."

"Great idea," I said. "What do you remember most about him?"

"I guess," Rocky said, "it was the time I was a cub and Grandpa Bear taught me to climb trees. At first I would put my little paws around the tree and then slide back down on my bottom. He and I got a good laugh out of that!"

"That's a wonderful memory," I said.

"And you know what," Rocky said, "when I'm a full-grown bear and have cubs of my own, I want to teach them to climb trees the same way."

"What a super way to keep Grandpa's memory alive," I said.

"Another thing I'll never forget," Rocky added, "Grandpa always taught me to tell the truth. I never forget that even when you ask me if I have been eating your blueberries!"

"By teaching you to tell the truth," I said, "Grandpa will always be a part of your life. If you and I didn't tell each other the truth, we couldn't be friends. And one more thing, even though you're sad, God will never let you go."

Scripture verse: "For I am convinced that neither death nor life ... nor anything else in all creation, will be able to separate us from the love of God in Christ Jesus our Lord" (Rom. 8:38,39).

Rocky and the Stranger

Yesterday Rocky was yawning when I asked him, "What's up, furry friend?"

"Oh, Dr. Bob," he replied, "let me tell you what happened to me not long ago. A rabbit came up to me and gave me a carrot to eat. It was really Robert Rabbit, but for some crazy reason I didn't know who he was."

"Did you eat the carrot?" I asked.

"Of course not!" Rocky replied. "I spit it out. Bears don't eat carrots!"

"Did you give him a gift, too?" I asked.

"Oh, yes," Rocky replied. "I gave him some honey, but he got it all over his fur. Boy, he was a sticky mess! I almost went back to my cave, but then I remembered what you told me one day. You said we ought to find something that both of us liked to do if we wanted to make new friends."

"So what did you do, Rocky?" I asked.

Rocky paused for a few seconds, then said, "Oh, I'll tell you. We decided to visit your blueberry bushes. I ate some blueberries, and the rabbit ate some leaves. Then we played hide-and-go-seek. That rabbit is one great player. I told him I had a wonderful time playing with him. And he said something that I found hard to believe, 'I'm Robert Rabbit!' "

"Well, Dr. Bob," Rocky added, "you could have knocked me over with a pine cone. At last I saw that it was Robert. He had been gone so long on a trip to the mountains where I grew up that I had forgotten him. Robert even brought me some news from home. He said my father was coming to see me this summer!"

"I'm so happy for you, Rocky," I said. "Your story reminds me a little of two people in the Bible who were walking along with a stranger one day. Only later, when they ate a meal together, did they finally see that the stranger was Jesus. And that was unusual because the two of them had known Jesus before he died."

"So what happened?" Rocky asked.

"Well," I said, "Jesus left them, but they were glad to know he would always be with them. They knew he was still alive. Even though they wouldn't be able to see him again, they could still see him through the people who loved him and believed in him. And we can, too."

Scripture verse: "Then their eyes were opened, and they recognized him, and he vanished from their sight" (Luke 24:31).

Rocky and the Animal with Everything

Rocky didn't hear me coming yesterday. He was looking at himself in the lake. I heard him saying, "Oh, what a handsome bear I am!" Suddenly he saw me, jumped up, and said, "Good morning, Dr. Bob."

"Morning, Rocky," I said. "What's happening around the ole barnyard today?"

"We're having another contest," Rocky replied excitedly. " This time we're having a *beauty* contest."

"Are you in it?" I asked.

"Absolutely!" Rocky said.

Soon the contest started. One by one the animals paraded by. The first animal to go by was Rocky Bear, strutting his stuff. Amy Aardvark, one of his big fans, said, "He's so cute! Surely he'll win."

Then Daniel Duck waddled by, showing off his beautiful feathers. "Hooray for Daniel!" several animals cheered.

At last it was Roberta Rabbit's turn. Dressed up like an Easter bunny, Roberta looked great. The crowd started buzzing because she dazzled everybody.

Finally, the head judge said, "The winner is . . . Roberta Rabbit. Her prize will be four bunches of carrots from the grocery store."

After the contest was over, Daniel Duck, ever the good sport, went up to tell Roberta how great she was. "You have it made around here, Roberta," he said. "You have everything!"

"No, Daniel, I don't," Roberta said. "You have such beautiful feathers and so many friends. I'm really very lonely here. I don't have any friends."

Rocky, who was listening nearby, said, "I never would have known that, Roberta. I didn't think you needed anything. Maybe you can go to church with us and make some friends. God will help, too. You won't ever have to be lonely again."

"Thanks, Rocky," Roberta said, "I'll try that. And it's great to have a friend like you!" Strangely, instead of feeling sad anymore because he had lost, Rocky felt good. He had made a new friend.

Scripture verse: "Cast all your anxiety on him, because he cares for you . . ." (1 Pet. 5:7).

Rocky Comes to the Party

Rocky," I said yesterday, "help me clean up the lot today. It's a big mess. Then Gail and I will throw a big party. Tell the other animals to help and to come to the party, too."

"All right!" Rocky said, jumping up and down, "It's a deal."

As the sun was coming up over the lake, Rocky and Daniel Duck started work. Rocky picked up dead tree limbs and put them in neat stacks. Daniel ate all the grass along the shoreline.

About lunchtime Ramola Bear showed up to work. She worked the rest of the day picking up tree limbs with Rocky.

Then about 5 o'clock in the afternoon, Robert Rabbit came to work. He had been looking for something to do all day and was glad to have some work to do. He worked until 6 o'clock, pulling up some ugly weeds. Then he quit when everybody else did.

When the animals finished, the lot looked beautiful. Soon they began to show up on our deck, asking, "Where's the party? We heard you were giving a party for everyone who worked on the lot."

"Welcome!" I said, greeting the animals. "Thank you for the hard work you did. In just a moment Gail will bring out some goodies." Soon Gail appeared with blueberry shortcake and strawberry punch for everyone.

But I noticed Rocky pouting by the door. "What's wrong, Rocky?" I asked.

"You gave the same party for everyone that you gave for Daniel and me," he whined. "We worked all day, but Robert showed up here at 5 o'clock, worked one measly hour, and still got invited to the party. It's not fair!"

"I know it seems that way, Rocky," I said, "but I treated you fairly. I gave you exactly what I promised . . . a party. You weren't upset until I invited Robert to the party also. Then you got upset. You don't seem to like it when good things happen to the other animals, only when they happen to you."

"I think Daniel and I should have had a bigger party!" Rocky said.

"Rocky," I said, "please know that I love you and Daniel, and I love Robert, too. I'm glad all of you could be here. There's enough food for everyone. Come to the party!"

Scripture verse: "Or are you envious because I am generous?" (Matt. 20:15b).

Rocky Is Loved

Rocky was really hurting yesterday. He had been climbing a tree when suddenly a limb broke, and he splashed into the lake. One of his paws hit a stump in the water. His paw was so sore that he was miserable.

Robert Rabbit hopped by and said, "Rocky, let's run over to Carthage today to see the Buggy Festival."

"Oh, Robert," Rocky said, "I can't do that right now. I hurt my paw when I fell into the water. It hurts a lot."

"I'm sure your paw will be fine," Robert said. "It couldn't hurt that much."

"Robert," Rocky replied, "how do you know how much my paw hurts? You don't live in *my* bear suit? Do you know what it feels like to hit your paw on a tree stump? No, I don't think you do!"

Then Amy Aardvark crawled by. She heard Robert and Rocky talking. "Rocky," she said, "I'm sorry you hurt your paw. I don't know what it feels like either, but I did hurt my snout one time on a briar. Say, you wait right here; I have a surprise for you!" And she ran off.

In a few minutes Amy returned with a snoutful of blueberries. "I picked these from Dr. Bob's blueberry bushes," she said. "Now watch this!" Amy mashed the blueberries into a paste. Going over to Rocky she said, "Hold out your paw!" When Rocky held out his paw, Amy put the blueberry paste on it. At that very moment Rocky's paw began to feel better.

"Thanks, Amy," Rocky said. "What a friend you are. Not only did you rescue me from the fire ants one day, but now you have helped my sore paw."

Robert Rabbit sneered, "Those blueberries won't do you any good, Rocky. Besides, I still don't think your paw hurts that much."

Later I asked Rocky how his paw was feeling. "Great," Rocky replied. "It's wonderful to have a friend like Amy. She reminds me of the way Jesus treated others in the Bible. But I would like to mash one of Robert's feet so he could see how much I hurt!"

"Jesus did try to help others when they were hurting," I said. "But he still loved others when they didn't say or do the right thing. So I hope you will keep on loving Robert Rabbit, too."

Scripture verse: "Do not repay anyone evil for evil . . ." (Rom. 12:17a).

Rocky Doesn't Like the Light

Yesterday, just before Gail and I went to bed, I heard a noise outside our front door. It sounded like a low roar so I knew it must be Rocky Bear. Sure enough, there he was, pawing at the front door.

"What's wrong, Rocky?" I asked, opening the door.

"Dr. Bob," he cried, "I heard a noise in the woods, and it scared me out of my wits. I don't know what it was. I saw that your lights were still on, so I thought I would knock."

"Come on in, Rocky," I said. "Would you like to spend the night here?"

"No," he answered, "I have to get back to the woods. I'll be sleeping all winter soon, and I have to get used to staying outside."

"Okay," I said. "And suppose I leave the spotlights on for the rest of the night. Would that help?"

"No, no!" Rocky said.

"Why not, Rocky?" I asked. "Wouldn't that keep you from being scared?"

"I guess it would," Rocky said, "but it would be bad in another way. I didn't want to tell you this, but if you leave your lights on you might be able to see me eating your blueberries!"

"So that's it," I said. "You like the darkness because you can sneak around and nobody can see what you're doing."

"Yes, yes," Rocky replied. "Sometimes the light is good because it helps me to see what I'm doing. But there are times when I don't like the light because I can't get away with anything!"

Laughing, I said, "I understand that quite well, Rocky. But just remember this: When you want to turn out the light to hide something, maybe it's something you really shouldn't be doing anyway. God wants us to live in the light so we don't need to hide what we're doing."

"Okay," Rocky said. "Leave your spotlights on for the rest of the night. Maybe they will remind me that God wants me to live in the light." Waving a big paw, he ran off into the night.

Scripture verse: "But those who do what is true come to the light, so that it may be clearly seen that their deeds have been done in God" (John 3:21).

Rocky Fusses at Himself

"Rocky," I said yesterday, "you remember Roberta Rabbit, don't you? She won the beauty contest for the best looking animal."

"Yes, I remember her," Rocky replied. "She's a real show animal. I don't like animals who think they're so great! And I don't like those thieving squirrels either. They steal all the acorns and hickory nuts in the woods."

"Anything else bothering you today, Rocky?" I asked, smiling.

"Yes, there is," Rocky replied. "What about the dogs around here? They are the laziest pack I have ever seen. All of them except Duke sleep all day!"

"My, my, Rocky," I said, "this really is an interesting talk we're having today. Roberta *is* stuck on herself, but I saw you looking at yourself in the lake last week."

"I know," Rocky said, "but I was only telling the truth when I said I was a handsome bear!"

"The squirrels *do* eat acorns and hickory nuts," I said, "but you eat up all my blueberries as soon as they get ripe."

"Oh," said Rocky, "I thought you were just sharing them with me!"

"The dogs *are* lazy," I said, "but you sleep six months out of every year!"

"I know that, Dr. Bob," Rocky said, "but I'm just a growing bear. I need lots and lots of sleep."

"You are right, Rocky," I said, "but I want to explain what has been happening this morning. You seem to find fault with others for things you do, too. Then you make wonderful excuses for everything you do, but you scold them for doing the very same things."

"I don't like what you're saying!" Rocky said.

"Well," I replied, "Jesus taught us to look at ourselves first before we say things about others. He also taught us to have mercy on them."

"I'll try to remember that," Rocky said. But with a twinkle in his eye he said, "Tell me why, Dr. Bob, every time you lose a tennis match, you never just admit you got beat!"

Scripture verse: "... first take the log out of your own eye, and then you will see clearly to take the speck out of your neighbor's eye" (Matt. 7:5b).

Rocky and Mother's Day

Rocky Bear was in a good mood yesterday except for one thing. He couldn't find his favorite blueberry yogurt at the grocery store. I said, "Rocky, did you remember your mother? Sunday is Mother's Day."

"Oops!" Rocky said. "I forgot about it. But what can I do at this late date?"

"Well," I said, scratching my head, "you can send her an e-card. Come on over to my house, and I'll show you how to do it on my computer." So Rocky and I went to my computer to pick out an e-card. He finally found one he liked.

Then I asked him, "Do you have her e-mail address?"

"Sure," he said, "it's 'mamabear@bol.com.'"

"What does 'bol' stand for, Rocky?" I asked.

Rocky said, " 'Bears online,' of course, Dr. Bob. All bears use that!"

"I should have figured that out, Rocky," I chuckled.

Rocky asked, "But why should I fool with this silly old e-card anyway, Dr. Bob? It's a waste of time. I could be eating or sleeping."

"C'mon, Rocky," I replied. "You can't be *that* hungry or *that* tired. Mother's Day is a time to honor your mother, to thank her for everything she did to help you grow up."

"Okay, okay, Dr. Bob," Rocky said, "but will you click it in for me? My paws are too big for the keys."

"Sure," I replied, clicking to send the e-card. "I know that will make her very happy." About ten minutes later, my computer chirped, "You've got mail!" An e-mail had just arrived from Mama Bear. I quickly opened it and read it to Rocky.

"Dear Rocky," the e-mail said, "Thanks for remembering me on Mother's Day. You're a terrific bear, and I'll always love you. By the way, I'm sending you some cookies by UBS, United Bear Service."

"Rocky," I said, "that sounds a lot like mothers. You try to do something nice for them, and they end up doing something nice for you!"

Scripture verse: "Honor your father and mother..." (Ex. 20:12a).

Rocky Doesn't Listen

Yesterday Rocky was talking a mile a minute to several of his friends. . . Amy, Billy, and Daniel. Rocky bragged, "Do you see that little birch tree over there? I can climb that tree in twenty seconds."

Daniel Duck laughed and said, "No way, Rocky. That tree is way too small for you to climb. I don't weigh three pounds, and it will hardly hold me."

"What do you know, Daniel?" Rocky said. "I come from a family of famous mountain tree climbers."

Billy Squirrel said, "Daniel is right, Rocky. I wouldn't try to climb that tree either. Birch limbs break very easily."

"I know you're an expert at climbing trees, Billy," Rocky fired back, "but you don't know how good I am!"

Amy Aardvark said, "I'll admit that I stick close to the ground or go underground to eat ants and termites. But Rocky, you weigh far too much to climb on those branches."

"C'mon, Amy," Rocky said. "Climbing trees is not in your bag of tricks. What do you know?"

So went the talk around Rocky's cave yesterday. It was clear to me as I heard them that Rocky wasn't going to listen to any of his friends. Then Rocky said, "Okay, I'll show all of you right now how to climb that tree. Just watch me!" And he began to climb as I started walking toward home.

Suddenly I heard a crack, then a loud splash. There was Rocky in the lake, swimming back to shore. The tree limb had broken, and Rocky took a swim he didn't expect to take.

The animals laughed and laughed. "Maybe you'll listen to us next time," they chanted as Rocky came up out of the water, shaking his fur.

As I sat down by Rocky, he said, "Guess I made a fool out of myself today."

"You were a funny sight," I replied, "but you're a good sport. Sometimes it pays to listen to what others say. No one of us knows everything, but all of us together know a lot of things.

"Once Jesus told his friends an important story. Then he said, 'Pay attention to what you hear.' In other words, there's so much we can learn from others if we will only listen."

Scripture verse: "Let anyone with ears listen!" (Matt. 13:9).

Rocky Gets a Surprise

Yesterday when I saw Rocky he was grinning. "Ah, furry friend," I said, "you're grinning from ear to ear."

"Oh, Dr. Bob," Rocky answered, "do I have a story to tell you! On Friday Ramola Bear and I were fishing from your dock."

"At least you two weren't eating my blueberries!" I joked.

"Suddenly," Rocky said, "something swallowed my hook and almost pulled me off the dock! I pulled as hard as I could. Ramola helped, too. Out of the water came a strange-looking creature. I said to him, 'My name is J. Rockwell Bear, and I'm boss around here. Please state your name.'"

"My name is Al E. Gator," the strange looking creature replied.

"I turned to Ramola," Rocky said, "and asked her if she had ever seen such a strange looking creature before."

Ramola said, "Oh, yes. In the coastal part of South Carolina where I came from, I've seen them before. They're *alligators.*"

"Oh, I get it," Rocky replied, "*Al E. Gator.* Well, Al," I told him, "I'm sure we'll get along fine as long you remember who's boss around here!"

"Okay, Mr. J. Rockwell Bear," Al said, "but let's get one thing straight. You may be the boss of the *land*, but I'm boss of the *water*!" When Rocky saw Al's teeth, he knew that Al meant what he said.

"So," I asked, "Rocky, why are you grinning today? It looks as if you would be upset because you're not the boss of everything."

"No, I'm not," Rocky said, "but I learned that surprising things happen just when you least expect it. There were Ramola and I fishing, minding our own business. And suddenly we met someone who changed our lives."

"How true," I replied. "People in the Bible met Jesus all the time . . . as they were fishing by the seashore, walking down the road and other places, too. Everything changed for them from that time on. Jesus became the most important friend they ever had."

Rocky said, "Now I know why you love to sing 'What a Friend We Have in Jesus!'"

Scripture verse: "And he said to them, 'Follow me, and I will make you fish for people'" (Matt. 4:19).

Rocky and Friends Go to a Picnic

Yesterday Rocky and my animal friends were excited, saying, "Dr. Bob, we're going to a picnic today at Brownson Church in Southern Pines! And we're going to walk."

"Great idea," I said. I watched them start out, wondering if they would ever make it. I knew it was a long way.

Robert Rabbit, perhaps the fastest animal, hopped way too fast going around a curve, ran into Mike Muskrat, and knocked both of them out. The animal rescue squad rushed to their side to give them first aid. When Robert woke up, he felt bad because he learned that Mike was going to a friend's birthday party.

Amy Aardvark didn't pay any attention to what she was doing. She first talked to Rocky Bear. Then she got out her cell phone and called her sister. Another time she stopped by the side of the road to eat some fire ants. Next she stopped at the end of a pond to look at her pretty red bow in the water. She looked at herself so long that the other animals passed out of sight. Amy then got on the wrong road and ended up in Aberdeen!

Rocky Bear told the other animals how to do everything. He tried to boss them. He was a real "backseat walker." He told them how fast to walk and complained about every move they made. Several times he got mad and slapped them with his paw. Once he got so mad that he had "animal road rage" and was arrested by the sheriff. It was an ugly sight!

Daniel Duck, however, was different. He said, "I'll just waddle along, saying, 'Quack, quack,' and obey all the walking rules. That way I'll get to the picnic, have fun, and not get upset. I don't have to get there first. I just want to get there safely."

And it was amazing how well Daniel's plan worked. They had to bring Robert Rabbit in on a stretcher. Amy didn't arrive from Aberdeen until an hour after the picnic started. And Rocky Bear was driven there by the sheriff who had put him in pawcuffs. Daniel alone showed that there was a right way and a wrong way to do things.

When the animals all came home last night, they told me about what happened on the way to the picnic. I asked Daniel how he had done so well. Daniel said, "I remembered that the Bible says, 'Your word is a lamp to my feet, and a light to my path.' I tried to do it God's way."

Scripture verse: "Your word is a lamp to my feet, and a light to my path" (Ps. 119:105).

Rocky Wants to Be Powerful

Rocky was standing up on his hind paws yesterday, flexing his muscles. He said, "We're having a contest this afternoon to see who is the strongest animal in North Carolina. Animals are coming from all over the state to take part. I'm sure I'll win."

"I'll come over," I said. "Who will the judges be?"

"Some of our church friends will help us," Rocky replied.

Rocky himself got the first chance to show how strong he was. He growled fiercely. Then he reached up and broke off a tree limb with his "bare" paws.

"Wow!" the crowd yelled. "Rocky is really strong. Nobody can beat him."

Marty Lion was next. He lived in a nearby national forest and came out to show his strength. Marty climbed a pine tree, then jumped about six feet and landed on the side of another tree.

"Unbelievable!" the crowd roared. "Maybe he will beat Rocky after all."

After Marty sat down, Larry Lamb stepped forth. He, too, came from the national forest. Beside the other animals, Larry looked weak indeed. He said, "I don't growl and break off tree limbs like Rocky. And I can't jump like Marty Lion either. I shouldn't even be here, but my friends made me come."

The judges asked Larry, "What can you do to show us how strong you are?"

Larry's friends spoke up and said, "Let us tell you about Larry. He doesn't like to show off. We were all late getting here because Larry stopped to help a rabbit who was lost. In fact, Larry helps more animals by being kind and loving than anybody we know. But he never says much about it."

The judges met for thirty minutes to decide the winner. Finally they said, "First prize goes to Larry Lamb! He has shown us what it means to be the strongest animal by helping the most animals. It's hard to build strong muscles but even harder and more important to help others. It's hard to stop thinking about yourself and to help them, but Larry did it."

At first Rocky was sad, but then he said, "Dr. Bob, I guess I'll just have to stop growling and start helping."

"Rocky," I replied, "maybe we should all do more of that!"

Scripture verse: "Blessed are the meek, for they will inherit the earth" (Matt. 5:5).

Rocky Comes Through for Father's Day

Rocky didn't even look up yesterday when I went over to see him. He was sitting under his favorite pine tree, thinking.

"Good morning, Rocky," I said, as cheerfully as I could. "You seem to be in deep thought today."

"Good morning, Dr. Bob," Rocky said. "Yes, I am in deep thought. I know that Sunday is Father's Day. I'm late in sending Papa Bear anything for his big day. As you know, I was late for Mother's Day, too."

"I have an idea," I said. "You could send him an e-card today to tell him you love him and that a present is on the way."

"Yes, yes," Rocky said excitedly, "but I'll have to borrow your computer again!"

"That's fine," I said, "but what will you send him for a gift?"

"I think I'll send him a jar of Sandhills honey," Rocky said. "Up there in the mountains he doesn't have anything except *sourwood* honey. Now, that's good, but I would like for him to try some of our *clover* honey."

"What a neat plan," I said. "I have a grandson who goes to college at Appalachian State University near your old home. We'll mail the honey to him and ask him to take it to your father."

"Great!" Rocky said.

My wife, Gail, then carefully wrapped the jar of honey, and we rushed out to mail it by United Bear Service. The man said it would arrive in the mountains by 10:00 A.M. on Sunday morning.

On Sunday morning we received an e-mail just before we left with Rocky to go to church. It came from Papa Bear.

Rocky put the e-mail in his big paws and read it: "Dear Rocky," it began, "Thanks so much for thinking of me today. You always were such a thoughtful young bear growing up. You brought me my bear slippers at night when I wanted to relax and read. We miss you but are glad you love the Sandhills so much. I will be down to visit you soon. Be sure to wish all the fathers at church a Happy Father's Day. And by the way, the clover honey is almost as good as our sourwood honey! Love, Papa Bear."

When Rocky finished the e-mail, I said, "Your parents have always loved you, and you have always loved them. That's really special."

Scripture verse: "Children, obey your parents in the Lord, for this is right" (Eph. 6:1).

Rocky Has a Problem

At first Rocky was quiet yesterday. I broke the silence by saying, "Rocky, my man, you seem unusually quiet for a Saturday morning."

"So you noticed, did you?" Rocky answered. "I didn't know you could tell."

"Tell what?" I replied. "All I could tell was that you were quiet."

"Oh," said Rocky, "I thought you could tell that I have the 'bothers' today."

"No," I said, "you just seemed to be thinking hard about something."

"That's right," Rocky said, "but I can't tell you about it."

"I see," I said. "Is it just too hard to talk about?"

"Yes, yes," Rocky replied. "I feel ashamed."

"I know how that is," I said. "Many times I've had a hard time talking to others about my problems."

"Not you, too, Dr. Bob!" Rocky said, somewhat surprised.

"You bet I have, Rocky," I replied. "But sometimes we just need to talk over things with others."

"Oh, okay," Rocky said, "but you've never heard anything like this! I sound fierce when I growl, but I really don't feel fierce at all. I'm scared of the dark. I'm a little clumsy. And I also eat too much. I just don't feel very good about myself today and much of the time."

"I'm glad you could tell me those things, Rocky," I replied. "It helps a lot when we are honest and trust other people to help us."

"You mean you can still be my friend even if you know all those bad things about me?" Rocky asked.

"Of course I'm still your friend, Rocky," I replied. "I've known those things about you for a long time, and yet I think you're a great bear!"

"Dr. Bob," Rocky said, "thanks for listening to me today and accepting me just as I am. I might still be afraid of the dark tonight, but somehow it won't seem so scary."

Scripture verse: "You desire truth in the inward being . . ." (Ps. 51:6a).

Rocky Can't Wait

What a fun time I had with Rocky yesterday! When I first saw him, he was very fidgety, squirming around as though he had sat on an anthill.

"What's up, Rocky?" I asked, trying to be helpful to my friend.

"Oh, Dr. Bob," he replied. "I can't wait until June 3."

"Why?" I asked. "What will happen then?"

"Don't you know?" Rocky asked. "School is out. And then I won't be able to wait until July 4."

"What special plans do you have for July 4?" I asked.

"Well," Rocky said, "the animals will have a big fireworks show around the lake. I love to watch the fireworks. And I can't wait for the beach party the week after that."

"Hmm," I said. "You seem to have a hard time waiting. In the meantime you're wishing your life away! What about this very moment? Isn't this a good time, too?"

"I see what you mean," Rocky said. "This *is* a good time for me. I have a lot to be thankful for. I'm a healthy, growing bear. I have a great place to live, and I have a lot of friends, too."

"Indeed, you do," I replied. "But I know it's fun to look forward to something we really want to do. And yet if we do that too much we forget all the good things God wants us to enjoy right now. Sometimes *those* things turn out to be the best things we ever do."

"All right," Rocky said, loping toward the lake. "This very day I can find somebody who needs my friendship, maybe Amy Aardvark. This very day I can clean up all the litter that others leave around here. And this very day I can send an e-card to somebody who needs cheering up."

"That sounds like good thinking to me, Rocky," I added.

"But you know what, Dr. Bob?" Rocky said. "I still can't wait until your blueberries get ripe again!"

Scripture verse: "Do not neglect to do good and to share what you have . . ." (Heb. 13:16a).

Rocky Lacks Self-Esteem

I saw Rocky about 10:00 A.M. yesterday. At first I couldn't find him anywhere. Then I heard a bear voice say, "Here I am, Dr. Bob. Look up!"

Looking toward the sky, I spotted Rocky high up in a longleaf pine. "What are you doing up there, Rocky?" I asked.

"I'm going to fly across the lake like Daniel Duck," Rocky replied. "If he can do it, I can do it, too."

"Wait a minute, Rocky," I said. "Daniel has a talent for flying. He was born to fly, but you weren't. You were born to do other things, like climbing trees, running fast, and should I say it, *eating blueberries?* Ducks can't do those things."

"Dr. Bob," Rocky replied, "you just don't get it! That little duck can do almost anything. He's a real star. He can swim and dive and fly like no other animal. And besides, he always does and says the right thing. No, if *he* can fly, *I* ought to be able to fly, too."

"It doesn't work that way in God's world," I said. "We can't do everything others can do. We have to learn to be happy with who *we* are."

"I'll show you," Rocky said. "Just watch me, and

you'll be amazed."Then Rocky leaped from the tree, flapped his paws, and . . . splashed into the lake, spraying water everywhere. He came up sputtering and swam to the shore.

As Rocky climbed up on the bank, I said, "Rocky, I have some good news and some bad news for you. Which do you want to hear first?"

"Give me the bad news first," Rocky replied.

I said, "The bad news is you found out you can't fly like Daniel Duck."

"Well," Rocky said, "what could the good news possibly be?"

"The good news is this," I said. "If you had tried to fly over land instead of water you might have fallen on a tree stump and broken your furry neck!"

"You're right," Rocky answered. "Maybe I had better be happy just being myself rather than trying to be like Daniel. After all, it's not bad being able to run fast, eat a ton of blueberries every year, and sleep for six months!"

Scripture verse: "We have gifts that differ according to the grace given to us . . ." (Rom. 12:6a).

Rocky Sees His Dad Get a Wakeup Call

As I approached Rocky's cave yesterday, I heard a loud noise. Then I saw a huge bear asleep in front of the cave. He was snoring! But who was he?

Rocky saw me coming. The big bear woke up at the same time. Rocky said, "Good morning, Dr. Bob. I want you to meet Papa Bear, who has come to visit from the mountains."

Papa Bear said, "Pleased to meet you, Dr. Bob. Rocky tells me you two are good friends."

"You bet we are," I said.

Then Papa Bear said, "Well, I think I'll take over around here since I'm the biggest animal in sight. Hey, you cottontail you," he said, speaking to Robert Rabbit as he hopped by, "don't run through this yard anymore!"

Turning to Amy Aardvark, he said, "Keep your long snout out of the anthills around here and go somewhere else."

To Daniel Duck Papa Bear said, "If I hear that 'Quack, quack' sound from you again, you'll be feathers for my pillow!"

Stunned, I said, "Wait a minute, Papa Bear. Who gave you the right to come in here and tell every animal what to do?"

"Listen, you preacher man," Papa Bear said, "I'm the biggest animal so that means I'm the boss. I tell everyone what to do, even you!"

"You'll see," I said. "Even if I have to call the Asheboro Zoo, you're not going to tell us what to do. The biggest have to live by rules, too."

Calming down, Papa Bear asked, "How do you do things around here?"

"Oh," I replied, "we talk things over and then vote on the best idea. Each animal gets one vote. The idea that gets the most votes wins."

"I never heard of such a thing!" Papa Bear said, his eyes about to pop out of his head. "But I'll behave because I don't want the zoo police to get me."

"You'll like our way of doing things once you get used to it," I said. "Every animal is free, and all are equal. We think God wants us to live like this."

So Papa Bear even decided to stay a few more days. He liked it here!

Scripture verse: "Let every person be subject to the governing authorities . . ." (Rom. 13:1a).

Rocky Wants to See God

Rocky was really angry with me late yesterday afternoon. Gail and I went with a group from the Jackson Springs Church to the Town Creek Indian Mound not far from our home. When we got back, we told Rocky what a good time we had. We also told him we saw a drawing of a bear on one of the Indian lodges.

"But why didn't you take me?" Rocky pouted.

"Because the trip wasn't a bear thing, Rocky," I replied, "it was a people thing. But I do want you go to church with us today. I have a special sermon about Jesus."

On the way to church, Rocky asked, "Why are you taking Amy Aardvark again? You take her almost as often as you take me!"

"Rocky," I replied, "Amy can help me explain something very important about God. She has claws as you do. When you see those claws, you know she must dig a lot."

"Okay," Rocky said, "but what does that have to do with God?"

"Hold on just a minute," I replied. "When you see Amy's long snout, you know she can burrow in the ground and eat ants and termites. When you see her floppy ears, you know she can hear what's going on around her."

"I know all that!" Rocky said, losing his patience. "So what?"

"When you read about Jesus," I said, "you learn how he helped the sick. He loved people who had no friends. He did brave things. When you see Jesus do those things, you see God at work."

"I still don't understand what Amy has to do with all of this," Rocky said.

I said, "When you see Amy at work, you know who she is by the things she does. Even though you can't see God, God showed us who he was by what he did through his son Jesus."

"I still wish I could see God," Rocky said.

"I guess we all do," I said. "But the thing that helps me is to read about what Jesus said and did. Seeing him is just like seeing God because he did what only God could and would do. He gives us a picture of God."

Scripture verse: "Whoever has seen me has seen the Father" (John 14:9b).

Rocky Meets Pablo

Yesterday Rocky was so excited he was standing on his hind paws again! "Dr. Bob," he began, "we had a surprise visitor last week."

"Who are you talking about?" I asked. "I didn't see any visitors."

"Why, Pablo Parrot!" Rocky exclaimed. "He came all the way from Guatemala. We needed some new birds around here. I get tired of robins and cardinals all the time. And are those other birds ever jealous of Pablo! He has such stunning feathers. They don't like it a bit that everybody stops and stares at him everywhere he flies. Nobody notices *them* anymore."

"Where is Pablo now?" I asked. "I'd like to see him."

"He likes to perch near that thick bamboo over there," Rocky said, taking me over to see Pablo. Pablo was a beautiful green and red bird indeed.

"Pablo," I said, "welcome! I hope you'll like it here."

"I do like it so far," Pablo said, "except some of the animals at school don't seem to like me very much. They are making it tough on me."

"I'm sorry to hear that," I said. "What are they doing?"

"They said they wouldn't play with me," Pablo answered, "because I was a stranger. They made fun of my green feathers. They also said my English wasn't too good because I had been speaking Spanish in Guatemala!"

"Now I can see why you are so nervous about school," I said. "But I know the teachers will help you get off to a good start. Some of the animals will help you, too. Several of them go to our church. They know that the Bible says, 'I was a stranger and you welcomed me.'"

Rocky said, "C'mon, Pablo. I want you to meet my friends who live around here. My feathered friend here is Daniel Duck. My hopping friend is Robert Rabbit. My digging friend is Amy Aardvark. And here's my special bear friend, Ramola Bear."

In a few days Pablo fit right in on the vacant lot. The last time I saw him he was teaching Rocky a little Spanish. Now I know why Rocky said, "Buenos dias,"—good morning—when I saw him today!

Scripture verse: "... I was a stranger and you welcomed me" (Matt. 25:35b).

Rocky Gets Down on Himself Again

Yesterday Rocky told me that all the birds and animals were having a big picnic to celebrate the end of summer. Pablo Parrot, who talked a lot, said to Rocky, "We birds can beat you animals in a game of softball."

"Ha, ha," laughed Rocky, "no way! We are much too strong for you. Most of you are very small."

"But we are also very fast, Rocky," Pablo replied. "We'll fly around the bases so fast you will only see a blur."

"You must be joking," Rocky said. "We could beat you if we had to bat with one paw!"

The game started. Soon it looked as if Rocky would be right. Robert Rabbit ran around the bases almost as fast as the birds could fly. And Amy Aardvark slugged a mighty home run. The score was 2-0 in favor of the animals until the birds came to bat for the last time.

Pablo got a hit. Daniel Duck got on base when Rocky made an error playing first base. Then Hank Heron knocked a pitch into the lake for a home run! The score was: Birds 3, Animals 2.

But the animals had one more chance. Billy Squirrel hit a single. Rocky stepped up to the plate, swinging a big bat. "Rocky can do it!" all the animals yelled. It was three balls and two strikes on Rocky. Pablo threw another pitch. Rocky swung with all his might and . . . struck out. Suddenly the game was over. The birds won.

"Dr. Bob," Rocky said sadly, "I failed. I can't do anything. And after I said all those things about how good we were, too."

"I know it's upsetting to you," I said. "but remember that God is still with you. And if you have God on your side, you will always be a winner. Even when you strike out, God is there to help you and encourage you. Also, as long as you try to help others, you will never be a failure."

A few days later Rocky was running toward Jackson Springs. As he passed a pond, he heard a baby rabbit crying out for help. Speedily, Rocky swam out and saved his life.

When I heard about it, I said, "Way to go, Rocky! By caring about others, you will always be a winner."

Scripture verse: "If God is for us, who is against us?" (Rom. 8:31b).

Rocky Seeks Revenge

Yesterday Rocky was really angry. "Why the scowl, Rocky?" I asked as I sat down by him on the lake bank.

"Well," Rocky replied, "I'm mad at Robert Rabbit again. He has done it now. He told Ramola Bear that I was pudgy. I didn't like that one little bit. Boy, am I going to fix that mean bunny!"

"What are you going to do, Rocky?" I asked.

"Oh, I've thought up a good plan," Rocky answered. "I know where Robert lives . . . in that hole in the ground near that dogwood tree over there. One night, after Robert goes to bed, I'm going to pour some honey down that hole. When Robert comes out in the morning, he'll get that sticky honey all over himself. Won't that be wonderful? How sweet it will be!"

"But Rocky," I said, "if you do that, then Robert will want to get even with you. Next, you will want to get even with him again. You don't have to get even, you can forgive him for what he did."

"*Forgive* that little cottontail?" Rocky shot back. "Never, never!"

"But all of us do the wrong thing once in a while," I said impatiently. "What would it be like if God never forgave us?"

"C'mon, Dr. Bob," Rocky said, "when was the last time *I* did anything wrong around the ole barnyard here?"

"Rocky," I replied, "just this morning I went out to pick some blueberries to put on my cereal. But there were no blueberries on my bushes. Hmm, Rocky, what's that ring of blue around your mouth?"

Rocky sputtered but finally said, "I figured it was all right for me to eat a *few* of your blueberries. I didn't think you would mind."

"Most of the time I don't," I said, "but this time I did. I told you always to ask me first before you ate my blueberries. You see, Rocky, all of us need to be forgiven sometimes. Maybe you can forgive Robert since you know that God is willing to forgive you."

"Okay," Rocky said, "I get it now. Maybe *I'll* just eat that honey tonight instead of pouring it down Robert's house!"

Scripture verse: "... be kind to one another, tenderhearted, forgiving one another, as God in Christ has forgiven you" (Eph. 4:32).

Rocky Tries to Improve

Rocky was eager to talk yesterday. "Dr. Bob," he began, "I've been a bad bear lately, and I really feel awful about it. I'm afraid God doesn't love me anymore. See, I have made a couple of posters to help me. The first one reminds me of the bad things I've done."

Curious, I looked at Rocky's first poster.

Poster 1

1. I ate Dr. Bob's blueberries and didn't ask him first.
2. I tattled on Robert Rabbit when I saw him eating a neighbor's carrots.
3. I said bad things about Daniel Duck because I was jealous of him.

I glanced at the list and said, "Rocky, at least you have tried to be honest about what you've done."

"Thank you, Dr. Bob," Rocky said, "I really do want to stop doing those things. So I made another poster of things I want to do to blot out the bad things and make God love me again."

Poster 2

1. I will pick up trash on the vacant lot.
2. I will be kind to Robert Rabbit.

3. I will send an e-mail to my parents every day for a week.

Rocky seemed pleased with himself and said, "Now God will forgive me for the bad things because my good deeds will cancel them out!"

"I see what you're trying to do here, Rocky," I said. "But just tell God what you've done and that you're sorry. God always forgives us. And then you can do those good things to thank God, not to make him forgive you. But if we try to do a good thing for every bad thing we do, we'll never be able to do enough."

"That just seems too easy!" Rocky protested.

"Ah," I replied, "it's not as easy as it seems. It's hard to admit you've done something wrong. And it's even harder not to do it again. Still, it's great that you *want* to do something to help yourself."

"Okay," Rocky said, "from now on, when God forgives me, I'll show God how thankful I am by doing a lot of good things."

"Rocky," I said, "I think we're getting somewhere now!"

Scripture verse: "... by grace you have been saved through faith ..." (Eph. 2:8a).

Rocky Learns about the Church

Rocky was reading his Bible yesterday when I went to see him. He seemed eager to talk.

"Dr. Bob," he began, "it says right here that the church is the body of Christ. How in the world could that be true? I just don't get it!"

"Say, Rocky," I answered, "you've given me an idea for a children's sermon tomorrow. Come on to church with us, and I'll use you to explain what the Bible means."

"No fair!" Rocky said. "Why can't you tell me now? I don't want to wait."

"I could tell you now, Rocky," I replied, "but I want it to be a surprise to you. We'll have fun."

"Oh, all right," Rocky said, "I'll wait, but you had better have a good story!"

At Community Church the next day the boys and girls came forward to see Rocky Bear just as they always did. I told them that I wanted to explain how the church was the body of Christ.

"Look at my friend Rocky Bear," I said. "His furry body does not have one part but many. And every part is important. Rocky needs every part." By now Rocky was smiling.

"Look at Rocky's nose, for example," I continued. "With his nose he can smell other animals when they come near his cave. With his eyes he can see them when they approach. And with his paws he can greet them and welcome them."

Rocky was thinking, "With my mouth I can eat more than all of these boys and girls put together!" He wondered what I would say next.

"Now, Rocky needs each part of his body," I said. "His eyes don't say to his paws, 'I have no need of you.' And his mouth doesn't say to his nose, 'I have no need of you.' Rocky uses every part of his body, but he's still only one bear.

"It's like that here at the church," I continued. "Each one of us has a part to play. One greets people, while another sings. One takes up the offering, while another preaches . . . and all of us come here to praise God and learn about God.

"Everyone is important. Everyone is needed. All of us together still make up one body. The Bible calls that body the church, the body of Christ."

Rocky was quiet for a while on the way home. Then he said, "I can't wait to get home and pick some more blueberries with my paws and eat them with my mouth!"

Scripture verse: "As it is, there are many members, yet one body" (1 Cor. 12:20).

Rocky Gets Mail

Yesterday we received a letter addressed to Mr. J. Rockwell Bear. At once I started looking for Rocky on the vacant lot. I finally found him snoozing away.

"Rocky," I said, "you got a letter today!"

Rocky quickly opened his letter with his big paws. It was from his first cousin, Bartholomew Bear, who now lived near Greensboro. There was a picture of "Bart," as Rocky called him, standing on someone's porch by a clothesline. Bart was pulling on the clothesline to get bags of lard that people had hung there to feed the birds.

"How clever of Bart," I said, "to figure out how to get that lard to eat."

Rocky said, "But I'm smarter than he is. I always beat him when we watch *Wheel of Fortune*."

"And what a good looking bear Bart is," I also said.

Rocky said, "But I'm better looking. Just look at my soft fur."

"Rocky," I said, "you don't seem to want me to say good things about your cousin. Why do you keep on saying that you are smarter and better looking than Bart?"

"Because I thought you would like him more than you like me," Rocky replied.

"No, no," I said, "I like you just as you are, Rocky. No one can take your place around here. You're our special friend. You're like part of our family."

"I'm glad to hear that, Dr. Bob," Rocky said. "When Bart and I were growing up in the mountains, he was always more popular than I was. He seemed to do everything right. Everybody liked him, and I felt left out. Even when our families got together, everyone wanted to talk about Bart."

"Now I understand how you feel, Rocky," I added. "I guess there's always someone around who makes us feel like that. Next time maybe you can stop and think about everything God has given you . . . a good family, good food, good health, and a good place to live. As long as you count *your* blessings, you won't worry as much about how God has blessed Bart."

"When Bart comes this summer to visit," asked Rocky, "is it okay for him to stay here?"

"Of course, Rocky," I replied, "and I'll even save a blueberry bush for him!"

Scripture verse: "Rejoice in the Lord always; again I will say, Rejoice" (Phil. 4:4).

Rocky Goes Home

Yesterday when I saw Rocky, he said, "Dr. Bob, I didn't want to tell you this, but I'm going back home to the mountains."

"But Rocky," I said, "I don't understand. I thought you were happy here living by the lake near us."

"Well, no, I'm not happy," Rocky replied. "You're okay, but I get bored around here sometimes. Daniel Duck likes to swim around, saying 'Quack, quack,' all the time. Robert Rabbit runs too fast for me. Even Ramola Bear says she doesn't like me anymore. So it's time for me to go back home."

"Okay, Rocky," I said. "I'll write your parents at 'bears online' to tell them you're coming home."

On Sunday morning, just before Gail and I left for church, there was a knock on our door. It was Rocky. "Thanks, Dr. Bob and Gail," he said, "thanks for everything." With that he loped on down the road and headed toward the mountains. Gail and I shed quite a few tears.

Almost a week passed. I just had to go over to the vacant lot on Saturday morning to think about the good times Rocky and I had enjoyed. I sat down by the lake where Rocky used to sit. I was so sad. Suddenly I heard a crunch, crunch, crunch in the leaves behind me. I looked back, and to my surprise there was . . . Rocky Bear! I was so happy that I gave him a bear hug. "What happened in the mountains, Rocky?" I asked.

"Things had changed a lot," Rocky said. "Some of the bears didn't even remember me. Another one told me the mountains were crowded with bears and for me to go back to the Sandhills. So I'm back here to stay."

"We're delighted to have you back, Rocky," I said, jumping for joy. "Maybe Gail will make you a blueberry pie, and we'll celebrate tonight. Sometimes we think things would be better if we went back to our old school or our old town, but it seldom is. We have to keep on doing new things and asking God to help us. And God will help us every time."

"I know that now, Dr. Bob," Rocky said. "Say, I think I'll go for a swim with Daniel." The last time I saw Rocky yesterday, he was swimming far out into the lake with Daniel, waving a big paw to all of us standing on the bank.

Ramola, who was also glad to see Rocky again, waved to him. It was great to have Rocky back on the vacant lot—to stay for good this time!

Scripture verse: "God is our refuge and strength, a very present help in trouble" (Ps. 46:1).

Printed in the United States
44639LVS00002B/269

9 780977 294138